Print Handwriting
Workbook

Handwriting
Workbooks
for kids

Print Handwriting Workbook
By: Handwriting Workbooks for Kids
ISBN: 978-1-944093-07-5

Table of Contents

The Uppercase Alphabet

A B C D E

F G H I J

K L M N O

P Q R S T

U V W X

Y Z

The Uppercase Alphabet

Follow the arrows to learn how to print the letters.

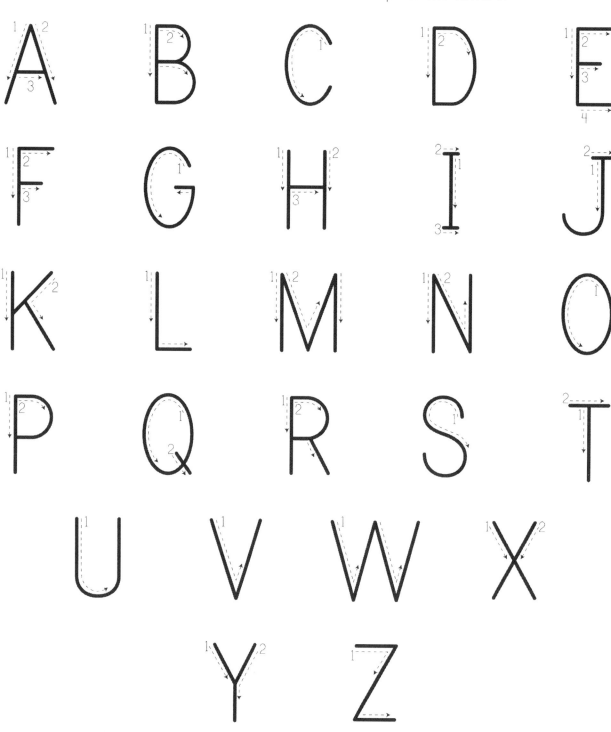

The Uppercase Alphabet

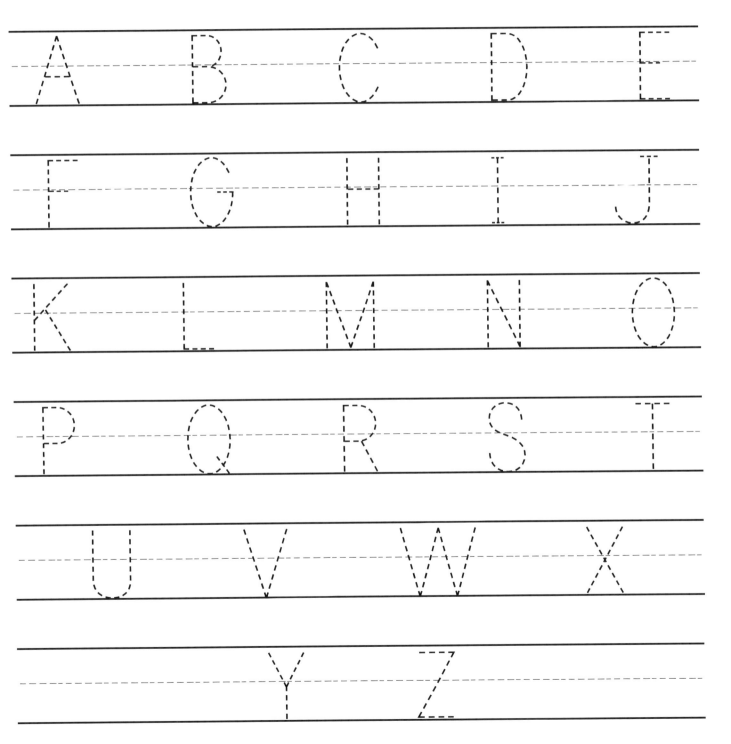

The Lowercase Alphabet

a b c d e

f g h i j

k l m n o

p q r s t

u v w x

y z

The Lowercase Alphabet

Follow the arrows to learn how to print the letters.

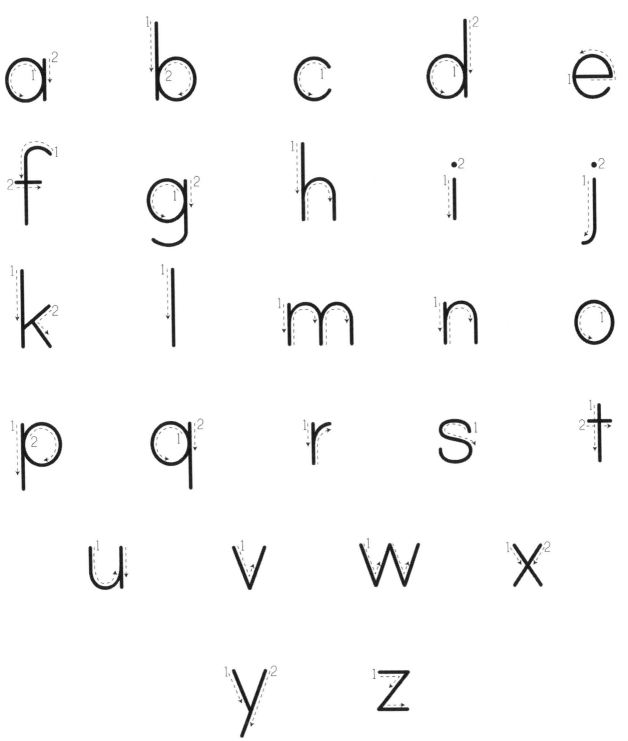

The Lowercase Alphabet

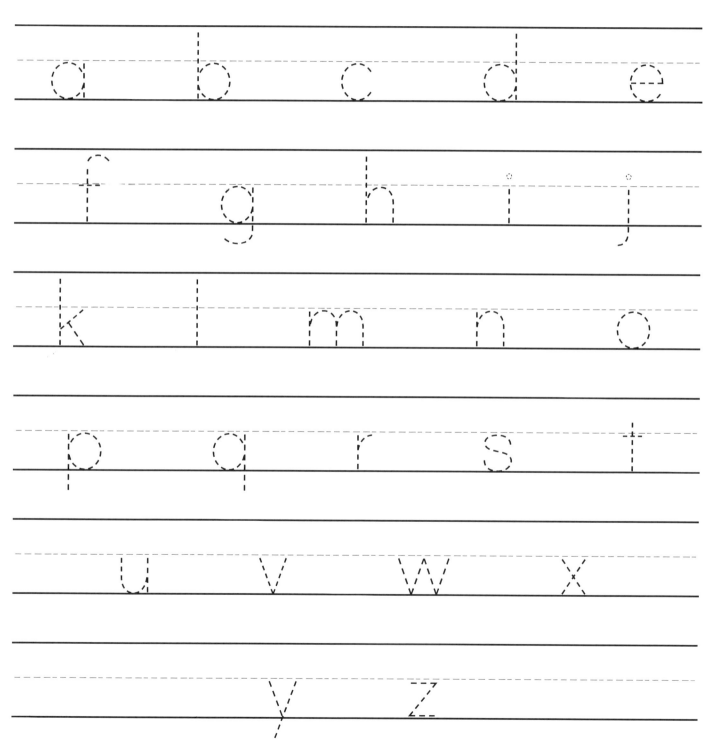

First, trace the letters and then try writing it on your own.

Bb

First, trace the letters and then try writing it on your own.

B B B B

B B B B

b b b b

b b b b

Cc

First, trace the letters and then try writing it on your own.

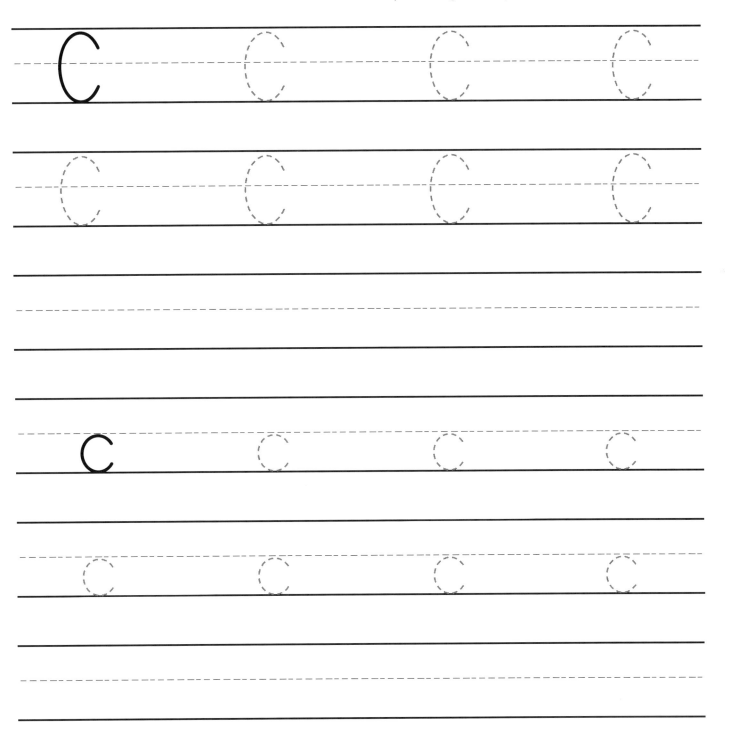

Dd

First, trace the letters and then try writing it on your own.

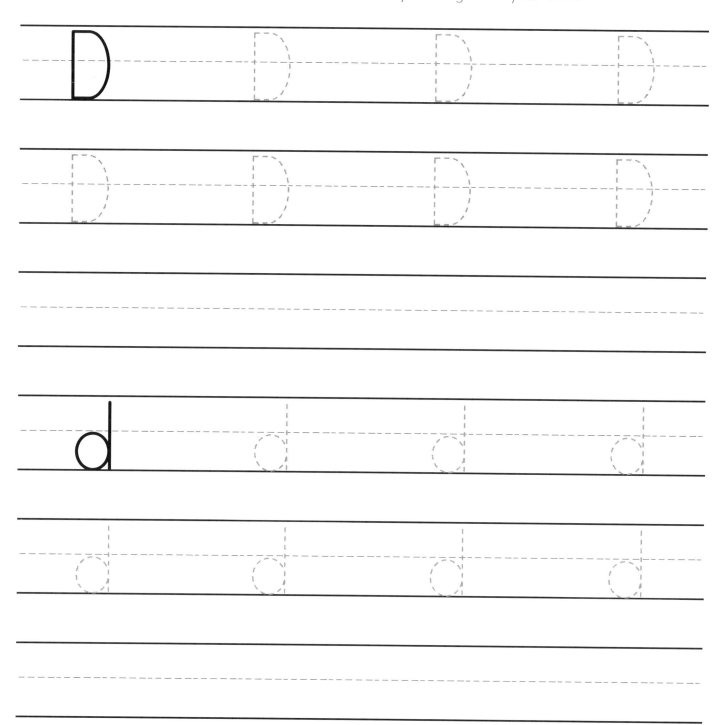

Ee

First, trace the letters and then try writing it on your own.

Ff

First, trace the letters and then try writing it on your own.

F

f

Gg

First, trace the letters and then try writing it on your own.

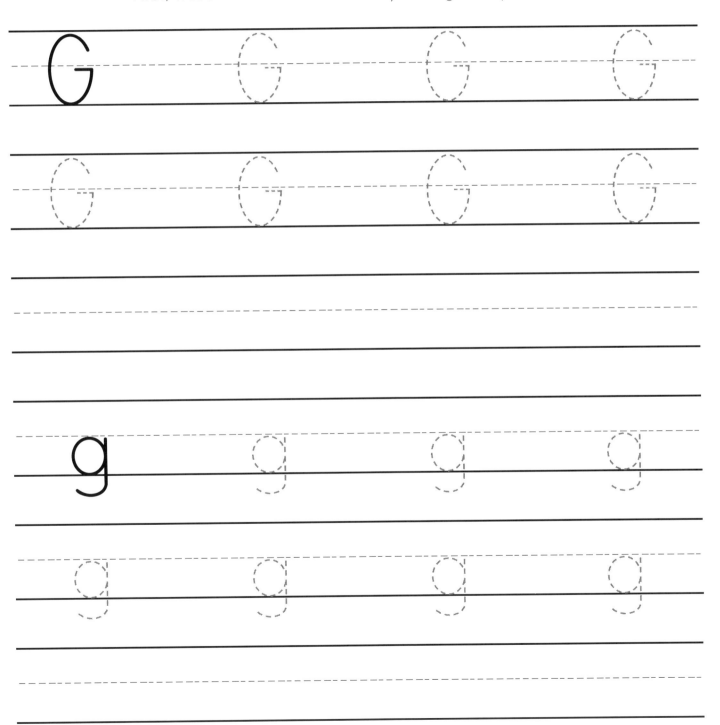

First, trace the letters and then try writing it on your own.

First, trace the letters and then try writing it on your own.

Jj

First, trace the letters and then try writing it on your own.

First, trace the letters and then try writing it on your own.

K

k

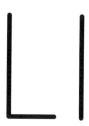

L l

First, trace the letters and then try writing it on your own.

Mm

First, trace the letters and then try writing it on your own.

M   M   M   M

M   M   M   M

m   m   m   m

m   m   m   m

First, trace the letters and then try writing it on your own.

N   N   N   N

N   N   N   N

n   n   n   n

n   n   n   n

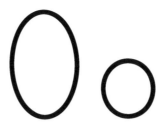

First, trace the letters and then try writing it on your own.

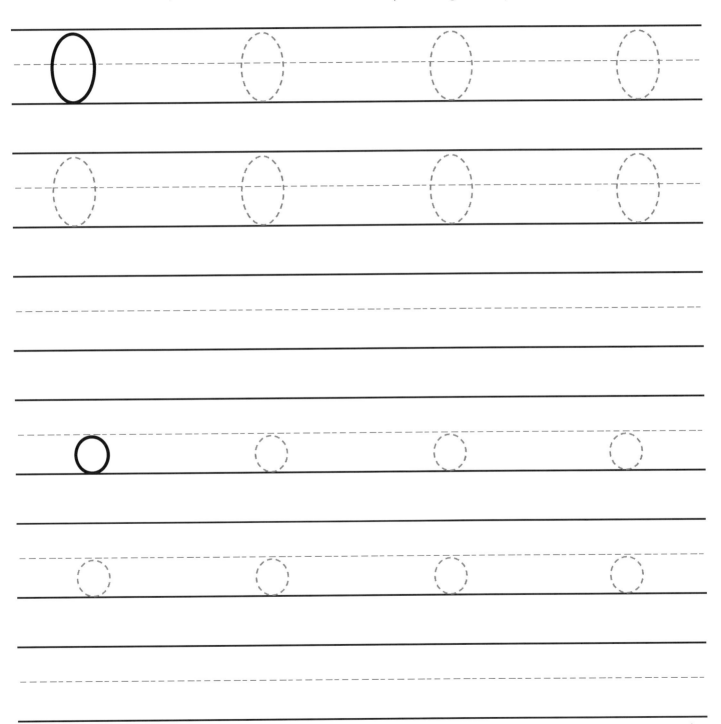

Pp

First, trace the letters and then try writing it on your own.

P   P   P   P

P   P   P   P

p   p   p   p

p   p   p   p

Qq

First, trace the letters and then try writing it on your own.

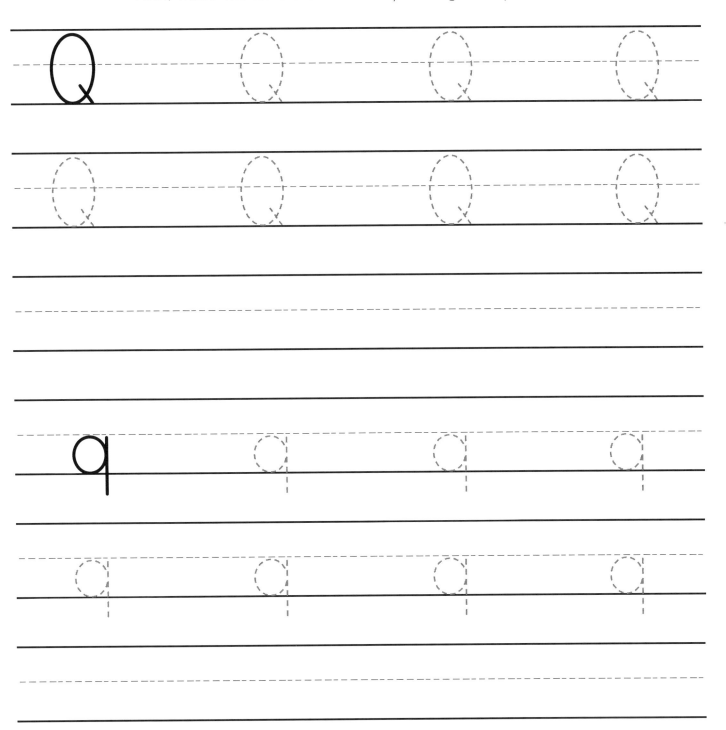

Rr

First, trace the letters and then try writing it on your own.

R R R R

R R R R

r r r r

r r r r

Ss

First, trace the letters and then try writing it on your own.

S   S   S   S

S   S   S   S

S   S   S   S

S   S   S   S

First, trace the letters and then try writing it on your own.

Uu

First, trace the letters and then try writing it on your own.

First, trace the letters and then try writing it on your own.

V

First, trace the letters and then try writing it on your own.

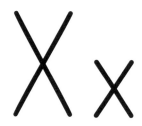

First, trace the letters and then try writing it on your own.

First, trace the letters and then try writing it on your own.

Zz

First, trace the letters and then try writing it on your own.

Z Z Z Z Z Z

Z Z Z Z Z

Z Z Z Z Z

z z z z

z z z z

z z z z

Writing Words

First, trace the words and then try writing it on your own.

apple   apple

apple

art   art   art

art

animal   animal

animal

Writing Words

First, trace the words and then try writing it on your own.

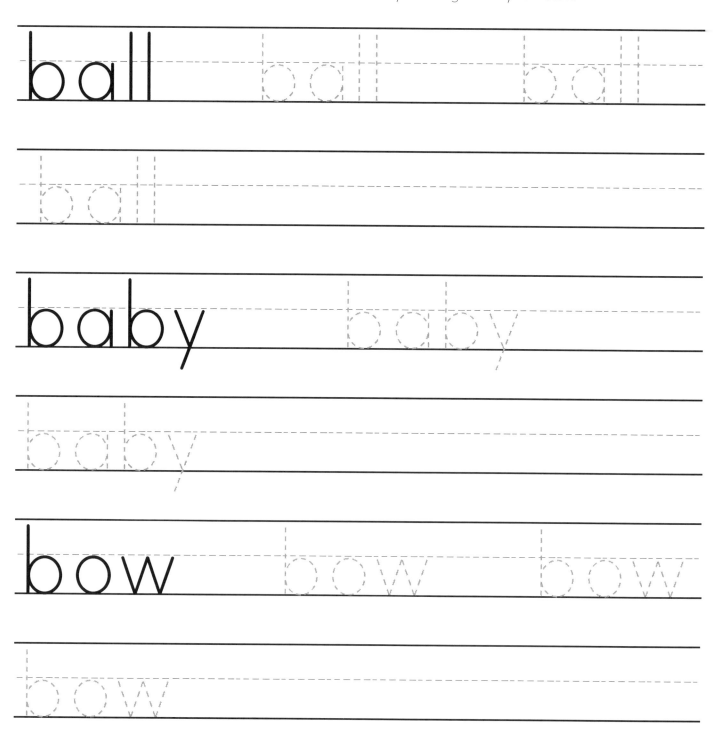

ball   ball   ball

ball

baby   baby

baby

bow   bow   bow

bow

Writing Words

First, trace the words and then try writing it on your own.

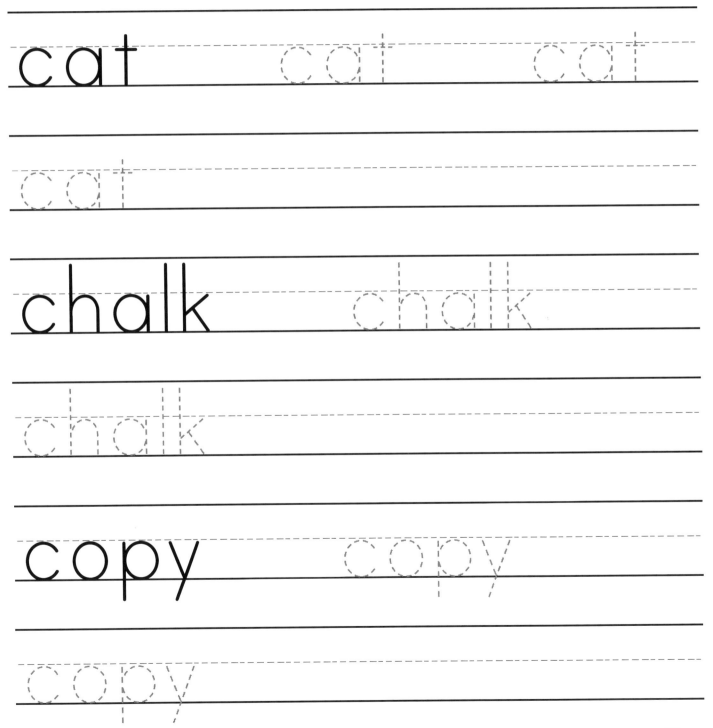

cat   cat   cat

cat

chalk   chalk

chalk

copy   copy

copy

Writing Words

First, trace the words and then try writing it on your own.

Writing Words

First, trace the words and then try writing it on your own.

ear   ear   ear

ear

exit   exit   exit

exit

end   end   end

end

Writing Words

First, trace the words and then try writing it on your own.

free   free   free

free

full   full   full

full

frog   frog   frog

frog

Writing Words

First, trace the words and then try writing it on your own.

goal   goal   goal

goal

green   green

green

gym   gym   gym

gym

Writing Words

First, trace the words and then try writing it on your own.

hero   hero   hero

hero

happy   happy   happy

happy

hug   hug   hug

hug

Writing Words

First, trace the words and then try writing it on your own.

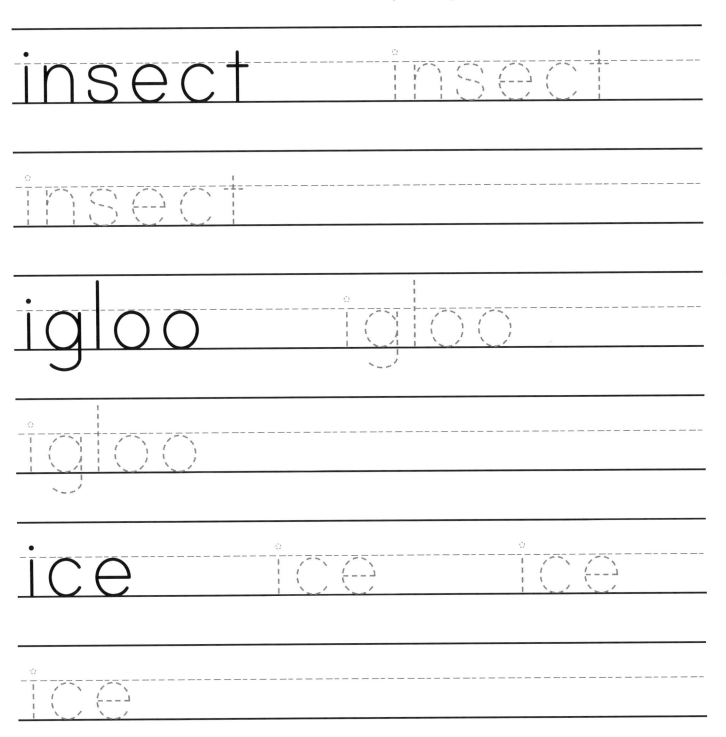

Writing Words

First, trace the words and then try writing it on your own.

Writing Words

First, trace the words and then try writing it on your own.

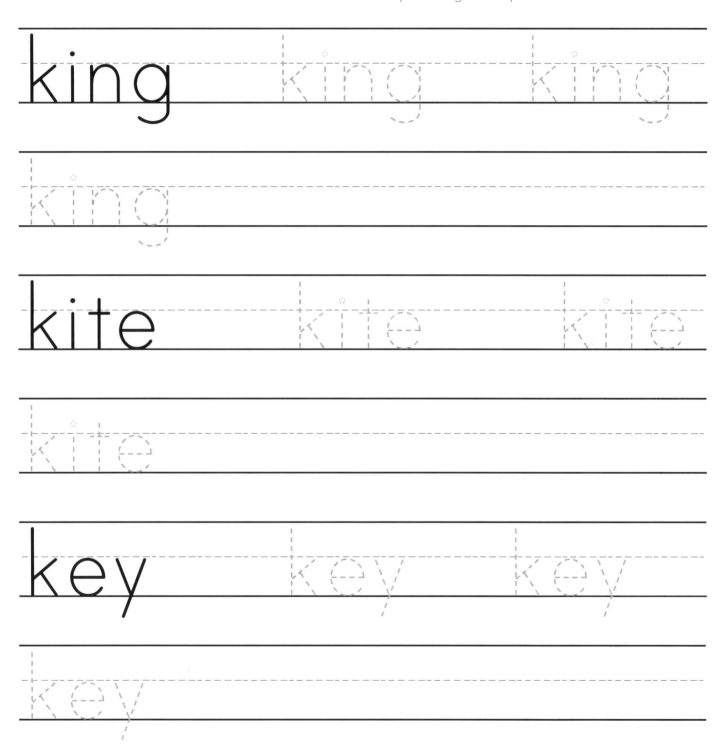

Writing Words

First, trace the words and then try writing it on your own.

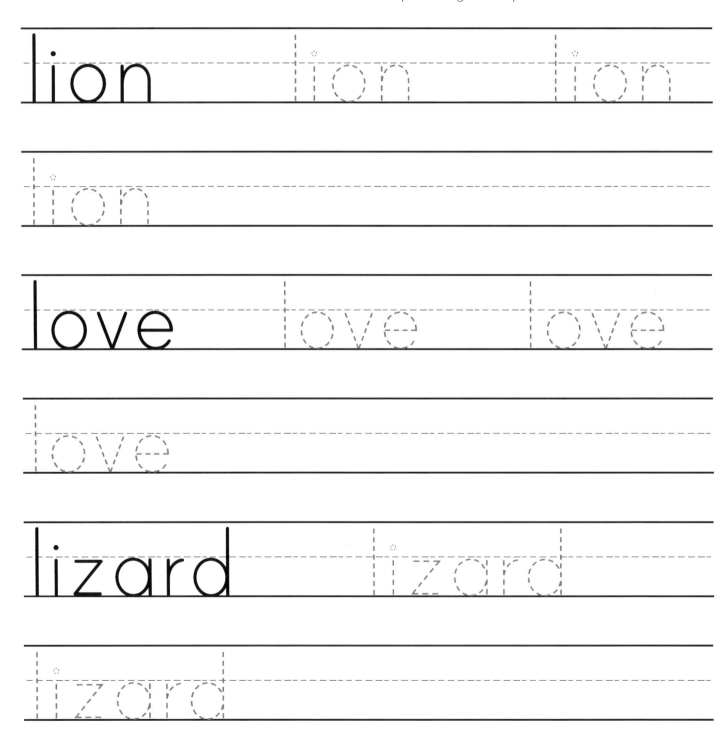

Writing Words

First, trace the words and then try writing it on your own.

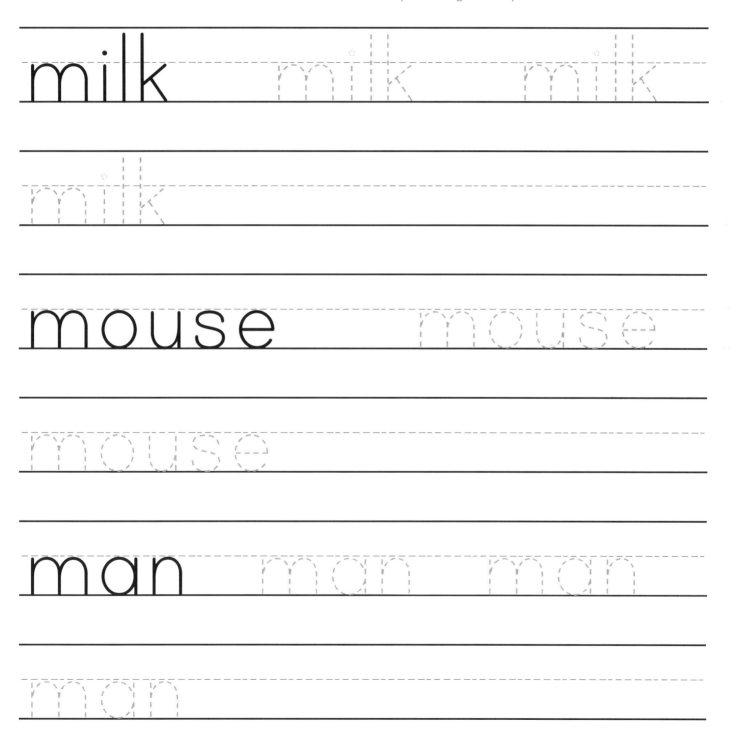

milk   milk   milk

milk

mouse   mouse

mouse

man   man   man

man

Writing Words

First, trace the words and then try writing it on your own.

nose   nose   nose

nose

net   net   net

net

nail   nail   nail

nail

Writing Words

First, trace the words and then try writing it on your own.

orange   orange

orange

owl   owl   owl

owl

ocean   ocean

ocean

Writing Words

First, trace the words and then try writing it on your own.

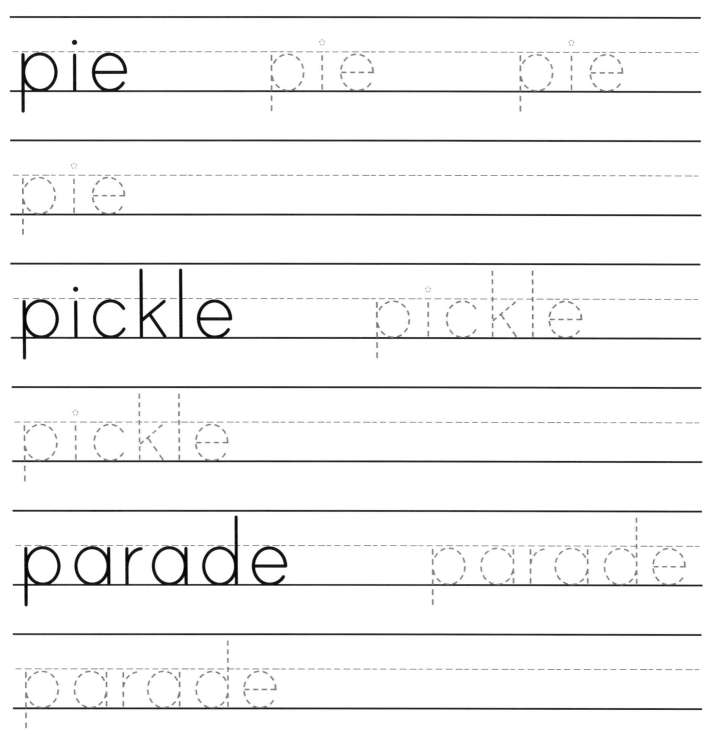

pie   pie   pie

pie

pickle   pickle

pickle

parade   parade

parade

Writing Words

First, trace the words and then try writing it on your own.

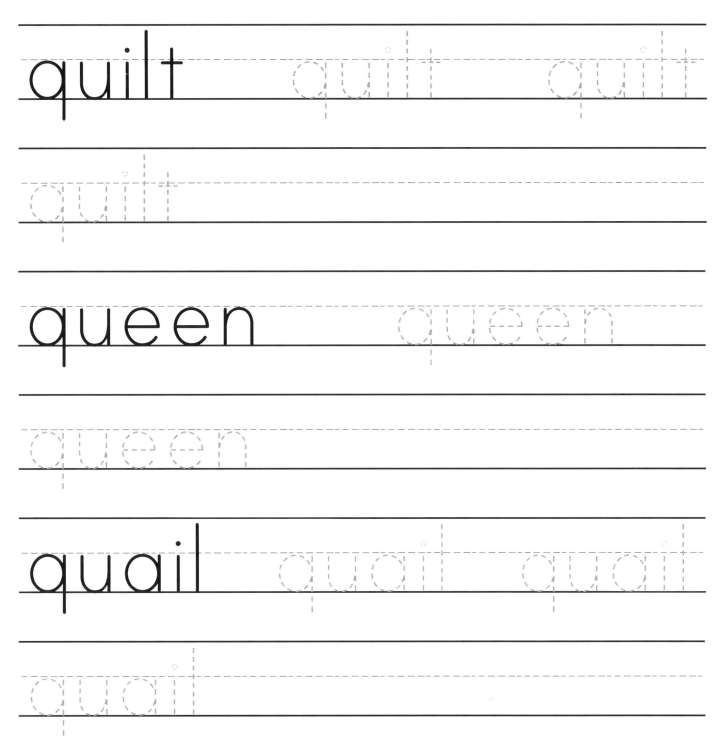

quilt   quilt   quilt

quilt

queen   queen

queen

quail   quail   quail

quail

Writing Words

First, trace the words and then try writing it on your own.

river   river   river

river

rope   rope   rope

rope

red   red   red

red

Writing Words

First, trace the words and then try writing it on your own.

sand   sand   sand

sand

sleep   sleep

sleep

scared   scared

scared

Writing Words

First, trace the words and then try writing it on your own.

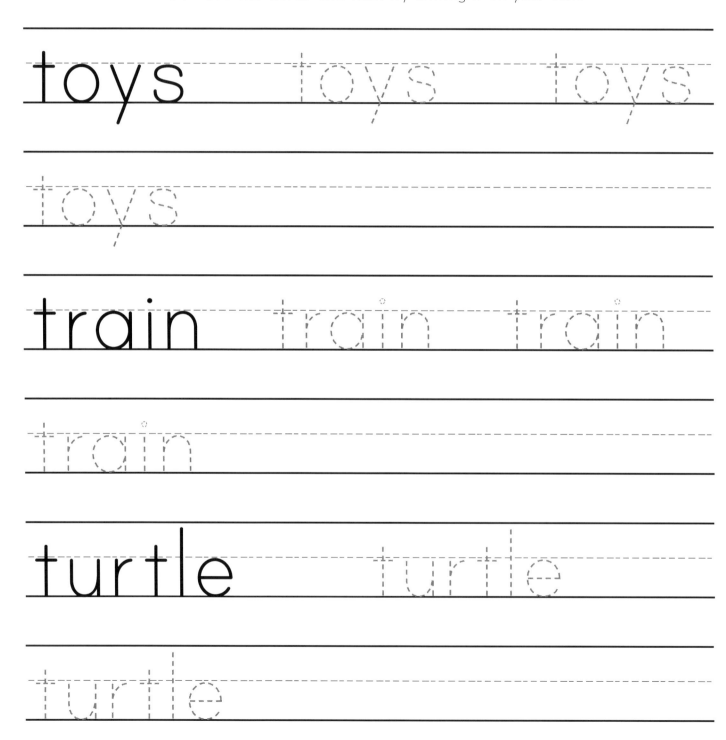

toys   toys   toys

toys

train   train   train

train

turtle   turtle

turtle

Writing Words

First, trace the words and then try writing it on your own.

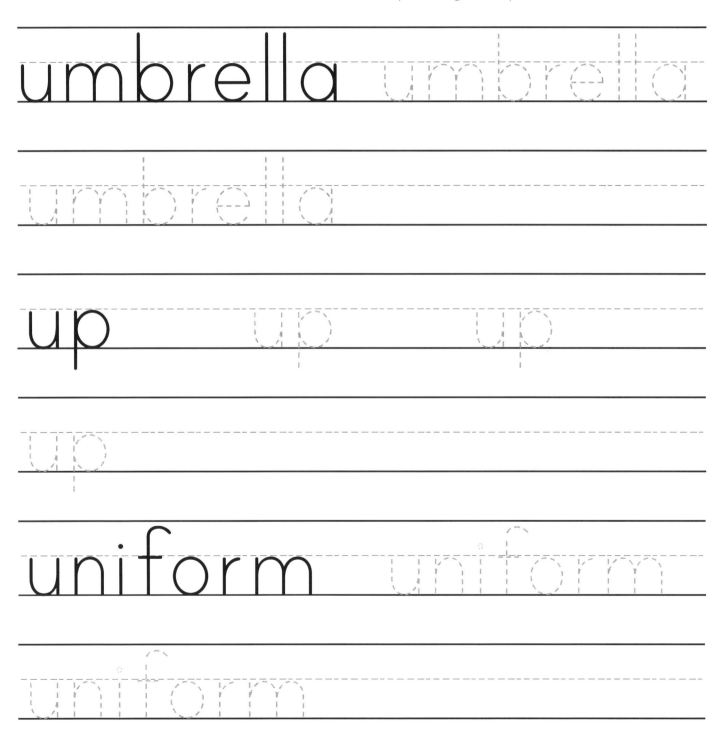

Writing Words

First, trace the words and then try writing it on your own.

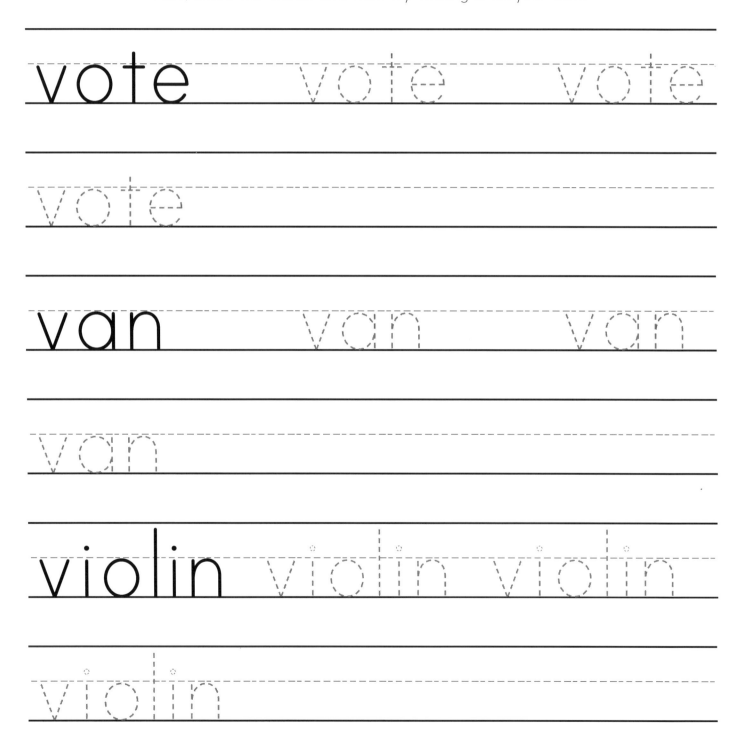

vote   vote   vote

vote

van   van   van

van

violin violin violin

violin

Writing Words

First, trace the words and then try writing it on your own.

worm   worm

worm

water   water

water

web   web   web

web

Writing Words

First, trace the words and then try writing it on your own.

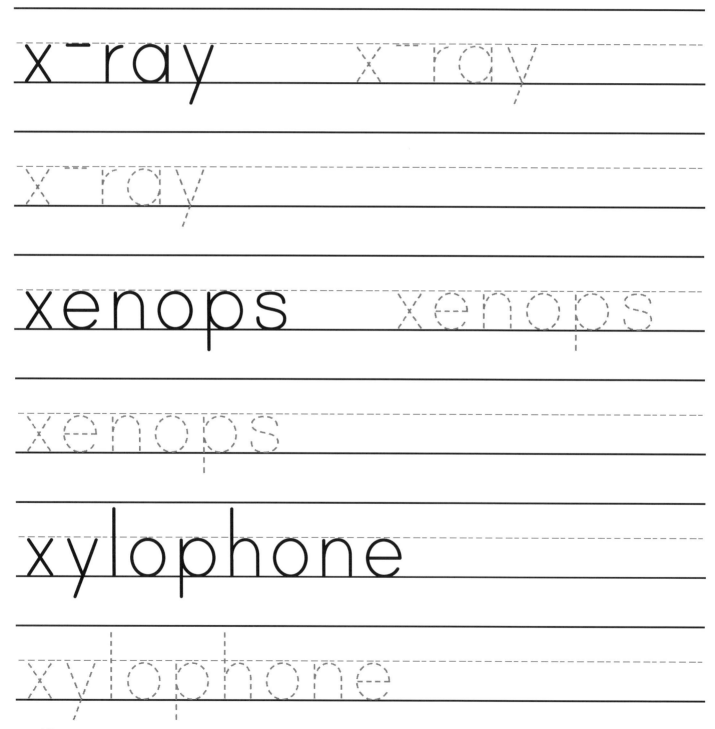

x-ray   x-ray

x-ray

xenops   xenops

xenops

xylophone

xylophone

60

Writing Words

First, trace the words and then try writing it on your own.

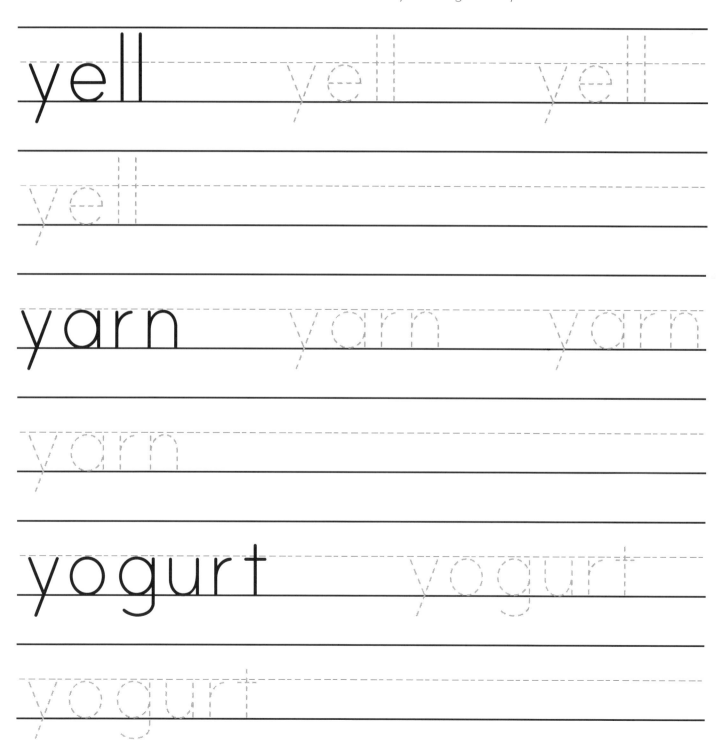

yell   yell   yell

yell

yarn   yarn   yarn

yarn

yogurt   yogurt

yogurt

Writing Words

First, trace the words and then try writing it on your own.

zebra   zebra

zebra

zoo   zoo   zoo

zoo

zero   zero   zero

zero

Days of the Week

First, trace the words and then try writing it on your own.

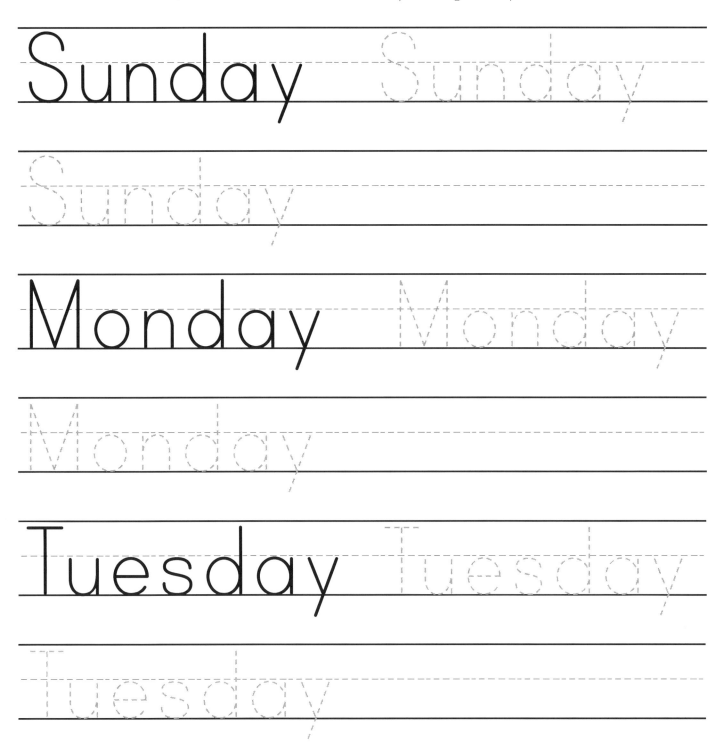

Sunday   Sunday

Sunday

Monday   Monday

Monday

Tuesday   Tuesday

Tuesday

Days of the Week

First, trace the words and then try writing it on your own.

Wednesday

Wednesday

Thursday

Thursday

Days of the Week

First, trace the words and then try writing it on your own.

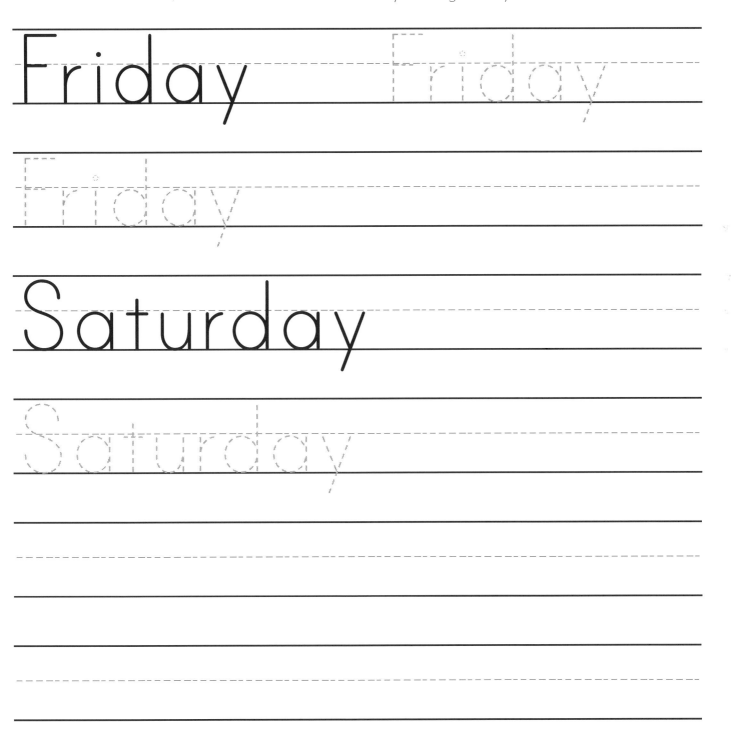

Friday   Friday

Friday

Saturday

Saturday

Months of the Year

First, trace the words and then try writing it on your own.

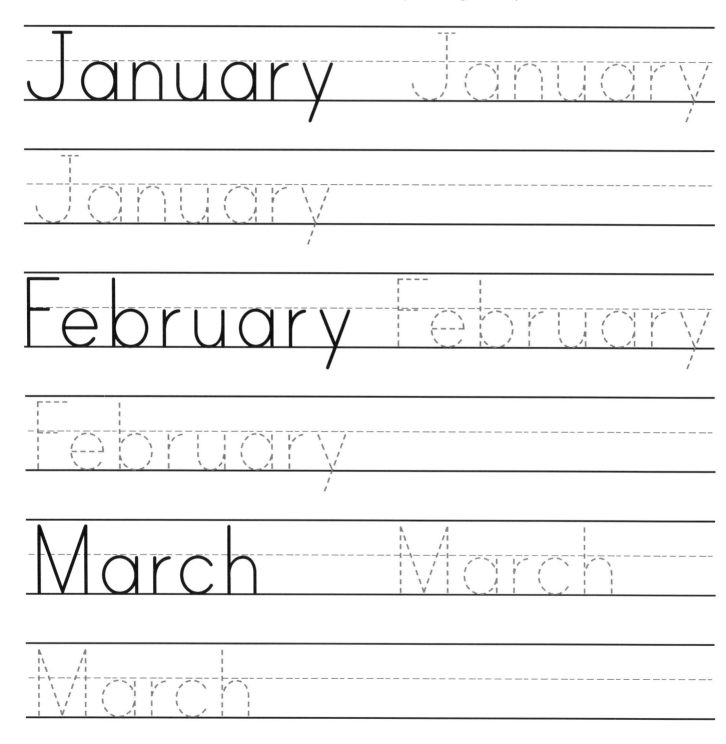

January   January

January

February   February

February

March   March

March

66

Months of the Year

First, trace the words and then try writing it on your own.

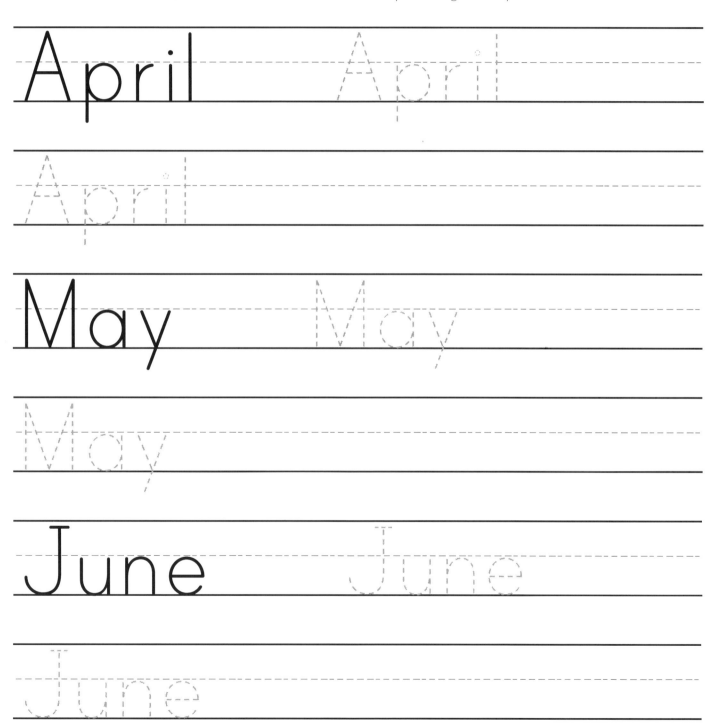

April   April

April

May   May

May

June   June

June

Months of the Year

First, trace the words and then try writing it on your own.

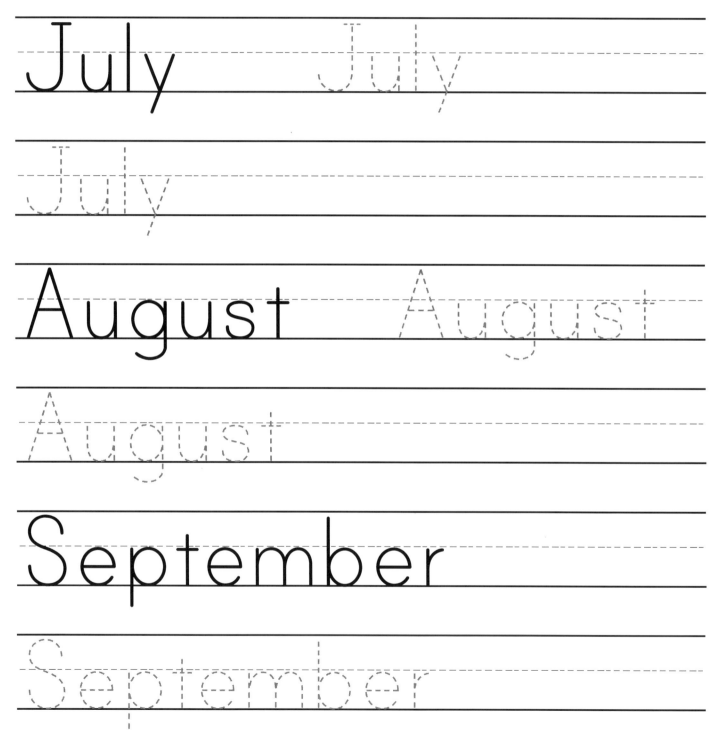

July   July

July

August   August

August

September

September

68

Months of the Year

First, trace the words and then try writing it on your own.

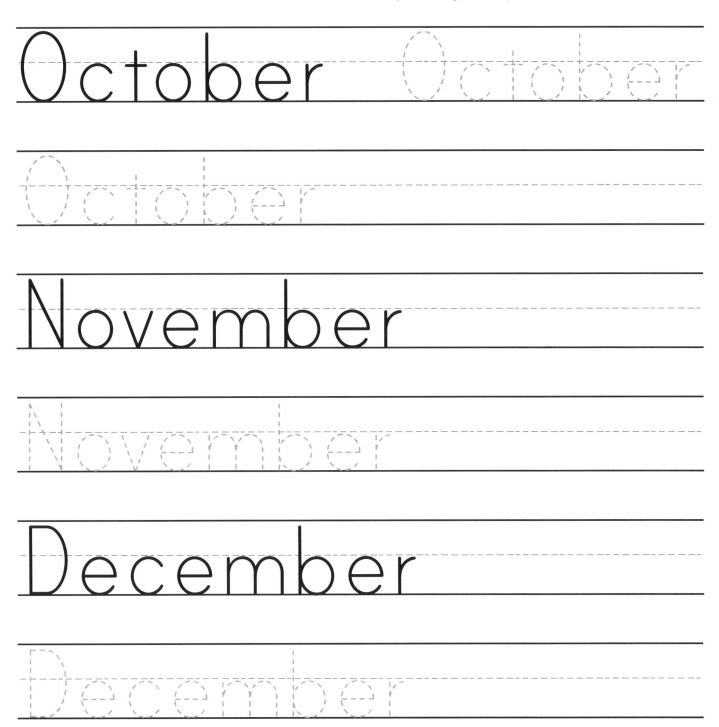

October

October

November

November

December

December

Writing Activity

All About Me

Fill in the blanks using your very best handwriting.

My name is:

Favorite color:

Favorite food:

Writing Activity

All About Me

Fill in the blanks using your very best handwriting.

Hobbies: _____

_____

_____

Favorite books: _____

_____

_____

Writing Activity

All About Me

Fill in the blanks using your very best handwriting.

My best friends:

_____

_____

_____

Favorite song:

_____

Numbers

First, trace the number and then try writing it on your own.

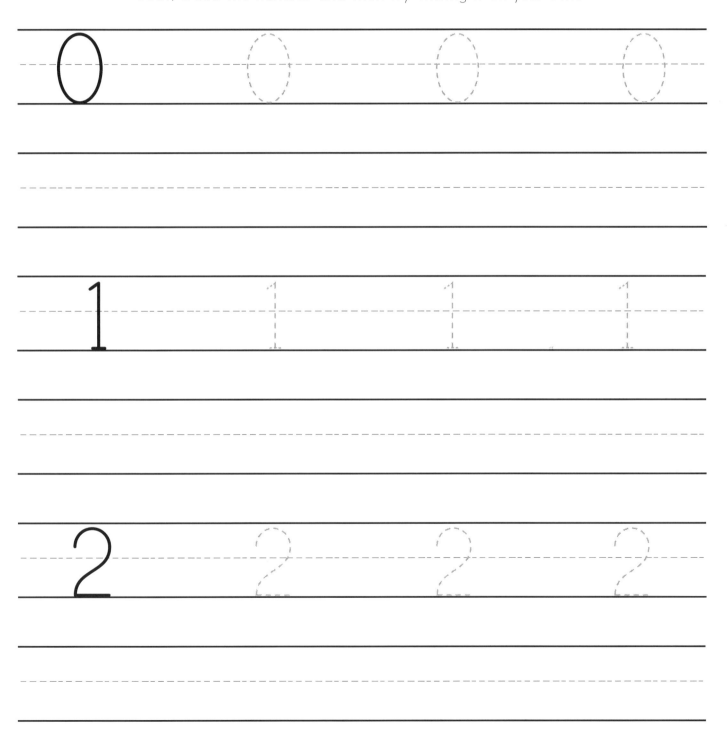

Numbers

First, trace the number and then try writing it on your own.

3   3   3   3

4   4   4   4

5   5   5   5

Numbers

First, trace the number and then try writing it on your own.

6   6   6   6

7   7   7   7

8   8   8   8

Numbers

First, trace the number and then try writing it on your own.

9   9   9   9

54378737R00051

Made in the USA
Lexington, KY
12 August 2016